Winnie the Pooh

Official Annual 1999

Editor: Lisa Carless • **Designer:** Jeanette Ryall

£5.99
UK Only

Hello, boys and girls!

Welcome to the Hundred Acre Wood. Why don't you join in our fun and games? Look out for the hidden pictures!

Contents

The indoor picnic

1 One morning, Pooh looked out of his window. "Today is just the right sort of day for a picnic," he thought. "And honey is just the right sort of food!"

2 "That honey pot's alive!" said Pooh, as it slipped out of his hand.

3 It bounce, bounce, bounced on to the table and straight into the picnic basket. "I wonder if my friend Piglet would like to come?" thought Pooh. Then he noticed a big, black rain cloud.

4 "If I hurry, I'll get to Piglet's house before it rains," puffed Pooh. But the rain was hurrying, too.

5 The rain soon caught up with Pooh. It plopped on to his nose and trickled down his neck. "Go away, raindrops!" he grumbled. Suddenly, some birds darted past Pooh, looking for shelter.

6 Pooh stumbled, and the honey pot toppled out of his basket!

7 The honey pot rolled away down a hill. "Come back!" cried Pooh, running after it.

8 Pooh ran and ran, but the pot rolled faster. Finally, it stopped outside Piglet's house. "Got you!" panted Pooh.

9 Piglet was so pleased to see Pooh. "I was just thinking that a rainy day should be shared with a friend," smiled Piglet.

10 Pooh stepped inside. "And I thought that it was a good day for a picnic," said Pooh, wiping himself dry. "But I was wrong!"

11 "It is a good day for an indoor picnic, though," said Piglet. "Let's lay this blanket on the floor and fetch the food."

12 "I think," said Pooh, "that an indoor picnic is the best picnic of all, especially when it's raining!"

HONEY

Drawing with Piglet

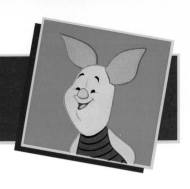

Can you help Piglet finish his drawing? Join the dashes and then colour the picture.

Rainy day rhyme

The rain falls down,
Pitter patter on the ground,
Making lots of puddles,
As it splashes all around.

● **What is Pooh eating?**

● **Where do you think rain comes from?**

10

The rain is very wet,

And it pours and pours,

But we don't mind,

We're picnicking indoors!

● **What colours are Piglet's curtains?**

● **How many raindrops are on the window?**

Woozle in the wood

1 Rabbit was in his garden getting really cross. Birds kept pecking at his lovely cabbages! "Go away!" he shouted, chasing the birds. "Shoo!"

2 "I've got to stop those birds eating my cabbages!" said Rabbit. Then he had an idea. He'd make **a scarecrow**!

3 When the scarecrow was finished, Rabbit put it in the middle of his cabbage patch. "**There!**" he grinned.

4 Later on, Tigger and Roo bounced by. "What's that in Rabbit's garden?" asked Roo. "It must be **a Woozle** stealing Rabbit's cabbages!" cried Tigger.

5 "Be **careful**!" shouted Roo, as Tigger bounded over to the scarecrow. "Don't worry, Tiggers know how to take care of Woozles!" replied Tigger.

6 Tigger bounced at the scarecrow and it fell to the ground. "**Got you**, Woozle!" he yelled. "Now leave those cabbages alone!"

7 Suddenly, Rabbit came running out of his house. "You silly Tigger! You've ruined my scarecrow!" he shouted angrily. "Oops, **sorry**!" said Tigger.

8 "How am I going to stop those greedy birds eating my cabbages, now?" demanded Rabbit. "But the birds have gone," said Roo. "**Look**!"

9 The birds were so frightened of Tigger they had all flown away. "**Well done**!" smiled Rabbit. "Tiggers make good scarecrows," said Tigger.

Rabbit's maze

Help Rabbit find the way back to his scarecrow.

Piglet's colouring

What colour are the cabbages?

What has Rabbit used for the scarecrow's nose?

Colour this picture with your pencils or crayons. Look at the little picture to see which colours to use.

How many birds can you see?

Can you think of a name for the scarecrow?

Cooling Owl

"Are you sitting comfortably, Pooh?" asked Christopher Robin. "Then I'll tell a story..."

It was such a hot day that Pooh and his friends decided to paddle in the stream. All except Owl, who said that owls didn't paddle in streams no matter how hot it was. So he sat alone on the river bank instead, and grumbled about the heat. "Would you like to borrow my sun hat, Owl?" asked Roo. "It will cool you down a bit."
"No, thank you, Roo," said Owl. "It's too small for me."
After a while he started grumbling again. "I'm still too hot," he said.
Pooh had a little think and then said,

"Maybe if we fan Owl with our leafy branches he will cool down a bit." So they flapped their fans very fast for a few minutes, getting very hot and bothered, but Owl still grumbled.
"You're making too much breeze," he complained. "It's ruffling my feathers!"

"Really, Tigger!" snapped Owl, shaking his feathers. "Now I'm soaking wet."
Just then, Kanga arrived with a tray of ice creams for everyone. "I thought you might need cooling down," she said kindly.
"I certainly do!" said Owl, tucking into his ice cream. "And this should do the trick!"
"I think that eating ice cream is the nicest way to cool down," said Pooh.
And everyone agreed with that.

"Did Owl cool down after that?" asked Pooh.
"Yes, he did," replied Christopher Robin. "And he wasn't grumpy any more. Goodnight, dearest Pooh."
"Goodnight, Christopher Robin. Now I'm going to have ice cream dreams!"

Rabbit scratched his whiskers thoughtfully. "Why don't you sit in the shade," he suggested. "Then you won't be so hot."
"But then I won't have anyone to talk to," muttered Owl.
"This will cool you down," said Tigger, splashing water over Owl.

Counting with Owl

How many bottles of pop can you see?

Can you count the sun hats?

Are there two or three pairs of sunglasses?

20

Drawing with Piglet

Can you help Piglet
finish his drawing?
Join the dashes and
then colour the picture.

Tigger's action rhyme

**Say the rhyme, then do the actions,
copying Tigger and Roo.**

Tigger fans himself when
it's hot,
Swish, swish, swosh,
Roo likes to play in
his tub,
Splish, splash, splosh!

Tigger has a long
cool drink,
Slurp, slurp, hic,
Roo likes an ice
cream cone,
Slurp, slurp, lick!

1 Pooh, Piglet and Rabbit decided to go camping. "Do you think Tigger would like to come?" asked Pooh. "Let's ask him," replied Piglet.

2 "No!" said Rabbit. "Tigger is too bouncy. He'll keep knocking the tent down. Let's hurry up before he sees us and wants to come!"

3 "Let's camp somewhere Tigger can find us," said Rabbit. "Wait for me!" panted Piglet, running to catch up.

4 "Goodness, Piglet. You are carrying a lot!" said Rabbit. "I know," sighed Piglet from under a big pile of things. But they carried on walking, looking for a sunny spot to camp.

5 At last, they found the perfect place. "Who's carrying the tent?" asked Rabbit. "Me, probably," said Piglet, toppling backwards with a bump!

6 Rabbit, Pooh and Piglet began to pitch the tent. "I don't think that's quite right," said Pooh, thinking hard.

So they tried again. "Pull your side of the canvas down!" shouted Rabbit to Piglet. "I need someone to pull me down!" yelped Piglet.

8 At last, the tent was up. "Now, where are the tent pegs?" asked Rabbit. He emptied out all of the bags but couldn't find them anywhere.

9 Then Rabbit had an idea. He used stones to hold the tent down instead. "Finished at last!" he said, proudly. "Oh good," gasped Piglet, feeling rather warm.

10 Just then, Tigger jumped by. "Ah, there you are!" he said, bouncing into Rabbit. "Oh no, it's Tigger!" groaned Rabbit, as he crashed into the tent.

11 "How did you find us?" asked Pooh, who was secretly rather pleased to see Tigger. "I followed the trail of tent pegs!" grinned Tigger. "Can I come camping, too?"

12 "Can he?" asked Piglet. "He did find the tent pegs, after all," said Pooh. "Please?" begged Tigger. So Rabbit agreed. Tigger was pleased!

27

Piglet's colouring

Colour this picture with your pencils or crayons. Look at the little picture to see which colours to use.

What is Piglet eating?

What colours are the toadstools?

28

How many flowers can you see?

Why shouldn't you go near fire?

29

The baby bird

"Are you sitting comfortably, Pooh?" asked Christopher Robin. "Then I'll tell you a story ..."

One sunny day, Piglet and Pooh were sitting out in Pooh's garden when they heard a squawking noise. They looked around and saw a baby bird hopping along the path, flapping its wings and crying out, loudly.
"Oh, dear, do you think it's hurt?" asked Piglet. Pooh watched the bird for a moment. The baby bird flapped its wings again and almost toppled over. Then it squawked, crossly. "Poor thing, I don't think it knows how to fly," said Piglet, looking a bit worried. "Maybe we can show it what to do," suggested Pooh. So Piglet and Pooh ran in front of the bird, flapping their arms. "Flap your wings like this, little bird!" shouted Piglet. "You can fly if you try!" said Pooh. The little bird hopped along the path, flapping its wings with all its might but still it didn't fly. "Hey, that looks fun. Can I play, too?" said Tigger, bouncing into the garden and almost landing on the baby bird. The poor little bird screeched with fright - and **flew**

off. "Hooray! You've done it!" cheered Piglet and Pooh. "Well done, Tigger!" "Why? What did I do?" asked Tigger, looking puzzled. "You helped that little bird to fly," said Pooh. Just then the little bird flew back down and landed on Tigger's shoulder, as if he was thanking him. Then it flew away again.

"I'm glad the little bird learned to fly," said Pooh. "I wish I could fly, too. I'd fly right up to a cloud and sit on it." "Silly old Pooh," laughed Christopher Robin. "Bears don't fly!" "I know," yawned Pooh. "But they do dream. And I'm going to sleep and dream about fly-ing. Goodnight." "Goodnight, dear, Pooh."

Drawing with Piglet

Piglet is drawing a bird's nest. Help him draw the eggs in the nest then colour in the picture.

Tigger's surprise

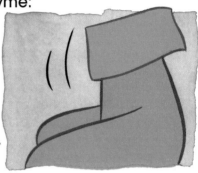

Here's Tigger to teach you a super rhyme. First, dampen two small pieces of paper, then put one on the index fingernail of each hand. Now copy Tigger here and say the rhyme:

1 Two little dicky birds sitting on the wall...

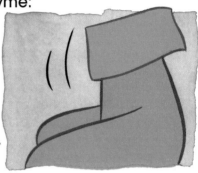

2 One named Peter...

3 ...and one named Paul.

4 Fly away, Peter.

5 Fly away, Paul.

6 Come back, Peter...

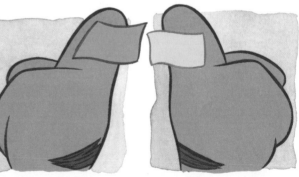

7 ...come back, Paul.

Pooh's nature notes

Hello, everyone. Today I'll be telling you all about woodpeckers.

This a Great Spotted Woodpecker. It has black and white feathers, white patches on its shoulders and red feathers under its tail.

Hello!

Point to the woodpeckers' tail.

Woodpeckers get their name from their noisy habit of pecking away on tree trunks with their strong beaks. They do this as many as ten times a second!

🐝 How do woodpeckers get their name?

Where's my dinner?

Woodpeckers make holes in tree trunks for their nests. When the baby chicks hatch, they poke their heads out of the nesting hole and cry for food.

🐝 How many birds can you see in the picture?

Buried treasure

1 Rabbit was digging his garden. Suddenly he noticed something shiny in the soil. "**What's that**?" he wondered.

2 It was the silver button that had dropped off his best jacket! "Yippee!" yelled Rabbit, going indoors. Tigger and Roo heard him shouting.

3 "Rabbit looks very pleased," said Tigger. "I wonder what he has found?" Piglet gave a squeak of excitement. "I bet he's found some buried treasure!" he cried.

4 "I wonder if there's lots of treasure in Rabbit's garden," said Tigger. "Come on. Let's see if we can find some, too!" Off they went to find some spades.

5 Tigger and Piglet began to dig for treasure. They dug and dug and dug! "Looking for treasure is very hard work!" puffed Piglet.

6 When Rabbit came out of his house he was very surprised to see Tigger and Piglet digging his garden! "Great!" he grinned.

7 "We didn't find any more treasure," said Piglet. "Keep digging!" cried Tigger. "We'll find some soon - just like Rabbit did."

8 Rabbit was puzzled. "But I didn't find any treasure!" he said. "I found this." And he showed them the silver button. Tigger groaned. "All that hard work for a button!"

9 "Never mind!" laughed Rabbit. "My garden looks lovely!" And as a reward for all their hard work, Rabbit thought that Tigger and Piglet deserved a scrumptious tea!

Rabbit's maze

Rabbit has found a map! Can you help him find his way to the treasure chest?

Treasure hunt rhyme

Can you guess what Pooh's favourite treasure is?

We're on a treasure hunt,
Searching here and there,
There are lots of things to find,
They could be anywhere.

How many pine cones are on the ground?

40

Can you name three different kinds of flowers?

We're searching all the trees,
And every inch of ground,
We'll carry on looking,
Until everything is found!

What colour are the flowers?

The rescue

"Are you sitting comfortably, Pooh?" asked Christopher Robin. "Then I'll tell you what happened one windy day..."

A gale was blowing outside as Owl dozed in the armchair. Suddenly, a big crash woke him up. "Dear me, whatever was that?" he thought, hurrying over to the window. But Owl couldn't see through the glass. It was blocked by a large branch. He hurried to his front door and tried to open it, but the door was jammed! The fallen branch had wedged it shut. "I'm trapped!" thought Owl, miserably. He sat down and tried to think of a way to escape.

Owl was still thinking when Pooh and Piglet passed the tree house. They were very worried when they saw the big branch across Owl's house. "Are you all right, Owl?" they yelled. "Yes, but I'm trapped like a sardine in a tin!" shouted Owl. "Can you move the branch?" Pooh and Piglet tried to lift the branch, but it was much too heavy for a small bear and

an even smaller Piglet.
"Poor Owl!" said Pooh. "How are we going to rescue him?"
"Hello!" shouted Tigger, bouncing up to them. "Isn't it a windy day?" He bounced around a bit and then gave an extra big bounce on to the fallen branch. It wobbled like a diving board, pinging Piglet and Pooh in all directions, and then rolled gently away.

"Hello, Owl!" said Tigger, bouncing through Owl's front door.
Owl was delighted. "I'm free!" he cried. "You rescued me, Tigger!"
"Did I?" asked Tigger, surprised.
"Yes, you did," said Pooh and Piglet, climbing up to join them. "Well done, Tigger!"
So that is how Owl was rescued. And how Tigger's bouncing was useful, for once.

"Did the wind go away after that?" asked Pooh, sleepily.
"Oh yes," nodded Christopher Robin. "The wind was tired of blowing and went to sleep."
"I'm tired too," said Pooh. "Good night, Christopher Robin."
"Good night, dear old Pooh. Sweet dreams!"

43

Tigger's bubbles

Tigger says that the best thing to do on a windy day is blow bubbles! Why not ask a grown-up to help you make one of his brilliant bubble blowers?

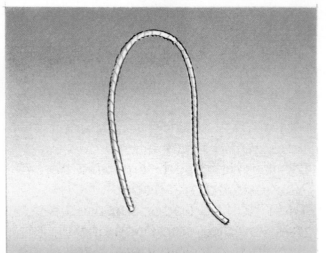

1. Bend a pipecleaner into a loop.

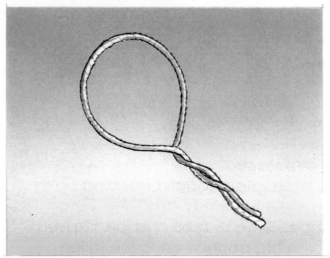

2. Twist the ends together.

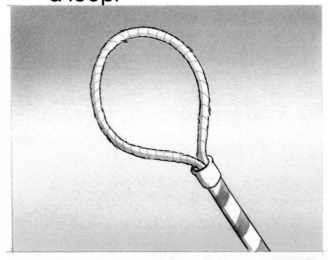

3. Push the ends into a drinking straw.

4. Dip it into some water and washing-up liquid. Now, blow!

Counting with Owl

● **How many windmills are there?**

● **Are there four or five leaves?**

● **Can you count the kites?**

Drawing with Piglet

Can you help Piglet finish his drawing? Join the dashes and then colour the picture.

The picnic story

1 Tigger, Roo and Rabbit were off on a picnic. Rabbit packed a big hamper of food. "Yummy," said Roo.

2 They all set off for the picnic. Tigger bounced in front and Roo hopped after him. "Wait for me!" shouted Rabbit, running after them.

3 Rabbit saw a nice, grassy spot. "Let's picnic here," he said. Tigger and Roo didn't want to. "Let's go a bit further," said Tigger.

4 So, off they went again. After a while, Rabbit was tired. "Let's stop and picnic here," he said. "No, not there," said Tigger.

5 Tigger and Roo bounced off again and Rabbit followed them. He was getting more and more tired and cross. "Slow down!" he cried. But Tigger and Roo kept going.

6 "That's it! I'm too tired to go any further!" Rabbit said, sitting down. "We're picnicking here and that's final!" But look what's happened ...

7   Rabbit sat on an ant hill! "Oh, no, ants!" he shouted. He jumped up and ran, trying to shake off the ants.

8   "Rabbit?" cried Tigger and Roo. "I thought you were tired!" They caught up and helped him brush off the ants.

9   Then Tigger realised that they were by the river. "Let's have our picnic here," he said. Rabbit was pleased. "At last!" he smiled.

The picnic rhyme

"Slow down!" called Rabbit,
"Wait for me!" he said.
But Tigger and Roo
Just bounced on ahead.

Who can you see
in the picture?

51

Piglet's colouring

Colour this picture with your pens, pencils or crayons.

 Who can you see in the picture?

 What colour is the picnic basket?

How many apples are there?

Have you ever been on a picnic?

Don't miss your favourite Disney characters in...

On sale every fortnight!

On sale every fortnight!

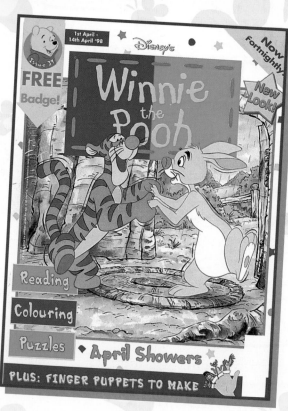

55

1 It had been a very cold night. "Brrr!" shivered Pooh Bear when he woke up. "It's so cold it must be snowing!"

2 Pooh ran over to the window. "The snow is so deep it's covering my window-sill!" he thought, worriedly.

3 "Oh, no, I must be snowed in!" cried Pooh. "I hope I've got plenty of food!" He ran downstairs to check how much he had.

4 Pooh was counting his jars of honey when someone knocked on the door. "It must be someone very big to walk through all that deep snow," trembled Pooh.

5 There was another knock. Pooh crept over and peered through the letterbox, right into a pair of eyes!

6 He opened the door. "Hello, Pooh," said Piglet. "Are you coming out to build a snowman?" "Oh, Piglet, it's you!" smiled Pooh, relieved.

7 Pooh was very pleased to find that he wasn't snowed in after all. So he dressed up warmly and went off with Piglet to build a snowman.

8 First, Piglet and Pooh made a big snowball for the snowman's body. "Do you think this is big enough?" asked Piglet. "Almost," said Pooh.

9 But the snowball rolled off down the hill, taking Piglet with it. "Help!" he cried. "Hang on!" shouted Pooh, running after him.

10 The snowball and Piglet rolled down the snowy hill. Then it crashed into Eeyore at the bottom. "That snowball could have hurt someone," grumbled Eeyore.

11 "Sorry, Eeyore," said Piglet as they both shook off the snow. "Pooh and I were making a snowman but it ran away!"

12 "Well, I think you've made a 'snowbear' instead," said Eeyore, pointing to Pooh, who was covered in snow. They all laughed.

Tigger's snowflake

Tigger wants to show you how to make your very own snowflakes! All you need is a circle of white paper, a pencil, some round-ended scissors and a grown-up to help you.

1. Draw around a cup on to a piece of paper and cut it out.

2. Carefully, fold the circle into four triangles like Tigger has done here.

3. Cut notches into the triangles with the scissors.

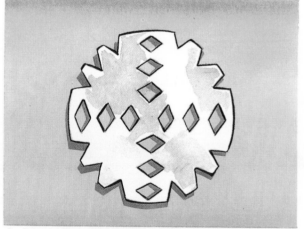

4. Unfold the snowflake and hang it up or stick it to a window.

Drawing with Piglet

Piglet is drawing a snowman but he isn't sure what to do next. Can you help him finish the picture?